A MILLION TIMES OVER
(A wasted love story)

A MILLION TIMES OVER
(A wasted love story)

SHUCHI BATRA

PAPER TOWNS
PUBLISHERS

PAPER TOWNS
P U B L I S H E R S

First published by
Papertowns Publishers
72, Vishwanath Dham Colony,
Niwaru Road, Jhotwara,
Jaipur, 302012

A Million Times Over: (A wasted love story)
Copyright © Shuchi Batra, 2021

ISBN Print Book - 978-93-91228-16-3

Printed in India

Dedication

To my husband, Manoj,
My mother, Vandana,
My in laws , Gokulavalsan and Prasanna,
My uncle, Pankaj, and aunt, Sangeetha,
My sisters, Sugandha and Vrinda,
My best friend -Deepika
My Instagram family.

She came in my life like a breeze
and left like a hurricane.
Never in my life
will I believe in fairy tales again

It's story of a boy named Siddhartha, a first-year engineering student who falls in love with Sia, his fellow classmate.

This story is based out of true events. This story will take you on a journey of highs and lows felt by this young couple who fell in love at first sight. They were spell bound by each other, but fate had something else written for them.

Quite often we read love stories with happily ever after, but none tells us what to do when the person whom we love leaves us in a maze. Who shall one reach out to, in such dark and hopeless days?

Let's read this story to find out what happened to them. Did they meet each other or become strangers again?

"I can't live without you"
to
"Who are you?"
we came a long way in this journey
called love

ACKNOWLEDGEMENT

I have been writing poems for many years, but writing a book and a story in the form of poems is a new experience for me. I would not have completed this book without the support of two important people: my mother and my partner. My mother has served as a guiding light throughout my life and has constantly encouraged me to take up writing. My partner showed me that true love exists and that happiness, from loving and being selflessly loved, is greater than anything else in this world. Without him, I would not have perceived the powerful emotions of love I have portrayed in this book.

I would also like to thank my artwork designer, Fathima Rehana.M, who brought life to the words through her art. Last but not the least, I would like to thank my dearest friends, Seema and Alaa, who proofread my book, listened to all my poems and provided valuable feedback to make me become a better author.

1.

THE FIRST TIME I EVER LAID MY EYES ON HER

It was the first time I had left my house for higher studies. I saw her for the first time at my fresher's party. She was completely different from any other girl that I had ever seen in my life. There was a mystery in her eyes which attracted me towards her.

Smokey eyes
colourful skies
smirked a little
gave me butterflies
you lit up wherever you go
come up here
my life needs some glow
I laid my eyes on her pretty face
her innocence enchanted
my happy space
Oh, I wish she agrees when I ask her out
I am feeling so nervous
I might pass out

2.

WANT TO ASK HER OUT

I had never asked anyone out. This was my first time. I was so shy and was feeling nervous just like any other teenager. My friends told me to go and try my luck. *But what will I say?* I thought. Shall I go or shall I pass on this chance that life was giving me?

Saw you once
want to see you again
please don't tell me
that you have some plan

3.

HIDING MY FEARS

Once I gathered the strength to approach her, my mind was bombarded with millions of fears. I have always loved romantic movies with happy endings, but what if mine did not turn out to be anything like the movies? With doubts in my mind, I walked across to her.

Walk with me
show me the sky
paint my universe
become my life

Not so easy
not so tough
like every love story
It has to be rough

Still, I asked her out
hiding my fears
behind my chest.
Please come in my arms
where you can rest

4.

THE FIRST DANCE
IN MOONLIGHT

She was looking at me from the corner of her eye while I was walking towards her. I just wished that she does not say no for a dance. We started with small talks, fake smiles and hearty laughs. The moon was shining exuberantly upon us. The sky was dancing with millions of stars and it was the perfect moment for me to ask her for our first dance.

She asked me
whether I had danced before
I said no
this would be my first one
her laughter
echoes till now
my heart was beating so fast
that its beats are still loud and clear

5.

WHAT WAS SPECIAL IN HER?

She gave me the vibe
and I know it was real
in this modern fake world
she looked crystal clear
almost surreal

6.

THE FIRST NIGHT OUT

She asked me to hold her in my arms. She started moving backwards and I followed her steps. I looked deep into her eyes, covering up my obvious feelings. I don't remember how long we danced. I was so captivated by her beauty that I forgot about my surroundings. I wanted to swim in the depth of her eyes which were telling me something. Suddenly, the music stopped. The party ended. We had to leave but none of us wanted to. We were happy, high and wanted to spend some more time.

The dance was over
we were asked to leave
she suddenly took my hand
and asked to sneak in
I followed her
Wherever she led me
If that is called love
Yes, I was falling for it
The night passed by,
we drank a bottle of wine,
she told me to come up on the terrace
without making any noise
passed the entire dusk
we waited for the dawn
will it be a beginning of a new story
or an incomplete song?

7.

THE FIRST TEXT:

We spoke about random things that first night. The uneasiness in the air evaporated with every passing second. We were basking beneath the sky. The moon and the stars were dancing while we were talking about our lives. It was a special kind of feeling where two unknown people suddenly form a connection, just like they show in movies.

Did not realize it was almost five
I said I had to leave
my class will start in some time
she told me to text her
once I reach my room,
the sun was about to rise
but I could still see the moon

I messaged her once I arrived
she replied in seconds
like she was waiting for it.
We spoke for the next 3 hours
and all the classes that I had that day,
I had to miss

8.

FIRST OF MANY THINGS

Days passed by and we became good friends. We wanted to try our first smoke and a drink. So, we made a secret plan where we did not tell anyone about our whereabouts. I went to her balcony during the night and we escaped the hostel. An adventurous night was about to start. *Let's see where it takes us*, I thought.

We smoked our first cigarette together
while we walked across the streets
she asked for the drink
and I laughed heartily

We took JD on the rocks
we were stumbling on the streets
I didn't know what was going to happen
I just wanted my first kiss

I tried searching for love
Whenever we would talk
I started feeling butterflies
Whenever we would go for a walk
How do I make her realize that
she was falling for me, too
If she won't tell herself
I would make her do so

9.

WAS I FALLING IN LOVE?

Your heartbeat
synced with mine
and I knew
I was in love
when I saw her for the first time

10.

WHEN I SANG MY FIRST EVER LOVE SONG:

I am not a singer by any means. But, when she asked me to sing for her, I could not have said no. So, I tried singing my first ever love song for whom I was falling every second. I wrote a song for her in a way that she could sense my inner feelings and get to know that what she means to me.

Take my hand
follow my lead
I'll show you the world
come play with me
I will tell you the stories
no one ever knew
because that's how I love
by showing everything on you

So let's lie down
slow down the time
you like some water
I will have some wine
let's go to Paris
see how romance is done
we'll lie on the streets
and jump in the sea
only then will we know
what love is likely to be

We'll crawl to the pubs
We'll dance on the roadside
We'll follow our guts
And chase the sunlight
We'll breathe in the air
Shout from the rooftops
Baby, let's pretend
We are happy
In our own world

Don't let any doubt
seep in your mind
Let's be crazy
And mad for a little time
Sit by my side
Play the songs while we drive
Shout from your lungs
Dance from within
Let the world know
You and I can survive

11.

LOVE WAS BLOSSOMING

As time was passing, we came closer to each other. She became my first hello and last goodbye. We would spend every possible second in each other's company. People started thinking we were a couple, but at that time, we were not dating. We were just friends who were afraid to take the next step. So, we both kept our feelings to ourselves to avoid getting hurt. It was difficult, but we tried. There was tension in the air, every time that we would come together. We could sense each other's feelings, but who would take the first step?

Never ending talks
during our walks
we both blushed
jumping butterflies
hard to hold in
uncontrollable smiles
trying to touch your skin
my heart jumping from within

12.

DAYDREAMING

I think everyone in their teenage has had reveries about someone special. I was no different. When she would not be around, I would rewind our memories and would make stories of our time spent together. She was in my mind for 24/7. I had never experienced this feeling; it gave me so many emotions in such a short span of time. With her I felt infinite.

I was falling in love
her name
reminded me
how lucky I was
that it fits in with mine so perfectly
like clouds merging into the sky
like sparkled nights
like the world was nothing
but infinite

13.

MORE THAN LOVE?

It was not about the intimacy,
kisses or fantasy,
she told me her secrets
which she had not told anyone before
and I don't know
what people think about it,
but for me it was more than love

14.

THE FIRST KISS:

The day came when I was about to confess my feelings to her.
I took her to a party. A romantic song started playing and I
asked her to dance with me. We came close to each other in
dim light. Her fragrance was pulling me towards her. I have
no memory of how long the kiss lasted but it still tickles me
whenever I think about it.

I took her for a dance
thought I had a chance
I pulled her close to my face
looked into her eyes straight
kissed her lips
and she did not resist
felt like a lifetime.
Time stopped flowing
and I knew in that moment
she was never going to leave my life

15.

LOVE COMES WITH DOUBTS

That night we did not speak after the kiss. We felt awkward and avoided each other throughout the night. Maybe we were afraid to risk our friendship. I was so scared that night and hoped that she would not leave me because of one stupid kiss. I was regretting the decision to kiss her as I was so afraid, for the first time, that I might have messed things up. Too many doubts were ringing in my head.

Let's go and see the stars
the moon will be there, too
dancing up in the sky
Will you believe if I tell you something?
Will you judge if I show you my scars?
Will you also leave if I tell you the truth?
Or stay if I tell you the lies?

Breeze would touch our face
and we would sit outside
telling the flashbacks
in dim light
I promised I won't leave you
till the end of my life
and I hoped you won't leave me
when time won't be right

Her smile would melt my heart
in ways she could never know
and even if I want to
I didn't know how to show

16.

THE PROPOSAL

We became normal and avoided talking about the kiss. But I was feeling restless, so I decided to take the shot. I had to propose to her, I had to tell her about my feelings. I thought to tell her on the day we were going on summer vacation. I went to drop her to the railway station. I was having millions of doubts in my mind. Her train was delayed, so I got some time to confess what she meant to me.

I slipped a letter in her hand
while she was about to leave
her train was fifteen minutes delayed
and I felt at peace
and grateful for the extra minutes
I got to spend with her

As we approached towards the station
I asked her
Will you be my girlfriend?
I gazed at her like a small child
putting all my hopes
at her side

If she would have said no
I knew I would have cried
but she said, of course
"You make my world bright"

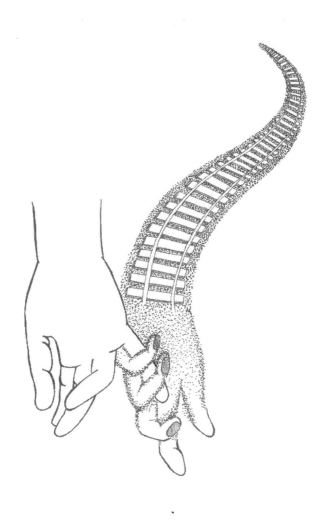

17.

WHY DO DISTANCES COME UP?

The happiest moment was also the saddest moment for me as she was leaving for her home for a three-month summer break. I was feeling helpless and there were not enough words to express my emotions.

So, here we were
standing at the station
gleefully enjoying
and then her train came
she wiped out my tears
and asked me to smile

But how could I be happy
when I knew that
we would be apart for a while
I wanted that moment to stop
to pull her on my side

But she had to go
and leave me
for some months.
Till then I would pretend
to be alright

18.

SHE LEFT ME AT THE STATION

With a kiss
on my cheeks
she left with a heavy heart
and wet eyes

I texted her the moment she entered the train and waited anxiously for her reply

Will you be my forever
and make me your life?
she said 'yes, for sure
you feel like home,
and that's more than enough
for me to survive'

19.

MONSTROUS DREAMS KILLING ME

Distance is tough, and for people who are newly love, it is like a monster. I used to feel anxious if we were not able to talk frequently. I would make up stories in my mind. I needed her to tell me that it was alright. So, I wrote:

I want to touch your skin
and whisper in your ears
the stories
that no one can hear

But I don't know if you are awake
I don't know if you are missing me
I don't know if to call
or stop imagining
the things
that are running in my mind
broken, like a loop
and I'm sitting by my window
waiting for the truth

Hope there is nothing to be afraid of
that nothing will break us apart
no one can come in between
please wake up once
and stop
my monstrous dreams
which are killing me
from within

20.

SHE CALLED ME
THE NEXT MORNING

I don't know when I fell asleep, but I when I woke up, my phone was ringing. I felt at peace.

She called
and all my fears disappeared
she made me go crazy
she made me go wild
she made me touch my soul
which I also did not know
existed within me
she touched a whole different side of me
and I hoped the journey with her
would continue till either one of us die

21.

HOPELESSLY ROMANTIC

There is not a day
when I don't think about you
Never a night
when I don't remember you
I don't know if you know this
but I am a hopeless romantic
who can't stop falling in love with you

22.

LONG DISTANCE RELATIONSHIP:

People say long distance relationship is tough to handle but it was not, because we were connected by a thread which was so strong that I never felt distant at all.

> We were at a distance
> but not distant at all.
> Two hearts, but just one
> soul

23.

WE MET AFTER 3 MONTHS
OF SUMMER BREAK:

Finally, the break got over and I was so excited to meet her. I felt butterflies in my stomach. The excitement to see her after three months was hard to explain

We were both dumb and young,
knew nothing,
souls craving for love

Give me a sign
I'll write you a letter
hold my hand
I will then whisper
tell the world
that we are together

In the end,
we were just eighteen
when we fell in love
and thought to build a world
in those crazy times

24.

DID YOU MISS ME?

Sia asked me if I missed her or not.
Look into my eyes and you would see
your face
open up my heart
and it will have your name
written on its every page

25.

DO YOU LOVE ME?

She asked me playfully, when we met. Three words; So simple yet so complicated. What is love, really? If you have to give a reason, then I think it's not love. Love is a feeling without any boundary or definition.

Siddhartha:

"I tried to get closer,
I whispered in her ears
you are all my reds
and definitely my blues
even if the world ends
I would still love you"

Sia:

"My darkest days
saw a hope of ray
when you whispered
'No matter what, I will always stay'"

I think I am cursed. Happiness does not stay with me for long.

26.

WHEN THE MASK COMES OFF

For once
in my lifetime
I thought
I had met someone real
and then her mask fell off

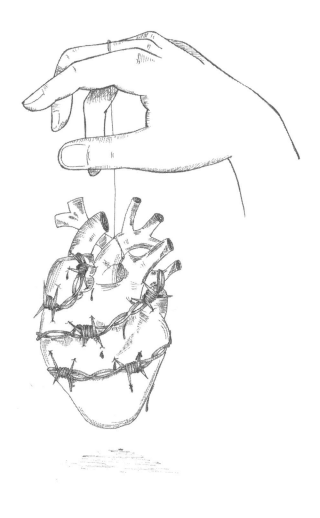

27.

WHEN I SAW HER TRUE COLOURS

After a while, I sensed a different side of hers. She was changing. She had recently put a lock on her phone. She was addicted to her phone even when I was by her side. I tried asking her, but each time she would try and change the topic.

Swirling my hands in your hair
the look of your gaze
went from stark
to blare

"Are you hiding anything?"
I asked you before it was too late
"No, everything is fine
he is just a mate"

Could not believe you for the first time
but tried to cover up
my doubts
just because I loved you
and would do so, till the end of my life

You took my hands
which were turning blue
Oh, your lies hurt
and now your presence was hurting too

28.

SHALL I PRETEND THAT THINGS ARE FINE?

I could not believe that my dreams were crashing down right in front of my eyes. I never imagined that someone whom I loved more than myself would eventually become the reason that I would not want to survive.

Should I walk up
and pretend to just leave?
When you are busy destroying me
planting doubts and fears of seeds

All the late-night blues
our snugly talks
were about to blow up in my face
and there you were, gazing me,
poisoning every word of yours
with sweet, sugar-coated lace

The biggest problem in my life was
I couldn't live without her.

48

29.

LET'S TALK FACE TO FACE

After a few days, I just could not control myself from asking her the truth. I expected what I was thinking was imaginary, but maybe it was not.

You blackened my days
darkened my nights
and when I said that I loved you,
You coldly looked into my eyes
making me sound so stupid
as if our love was nothing
but a game
now if you started it
and hence
you are the one to be blamed

30.

AND THE BLAME GAME STARTS

I asked her to tell the truth but instead she started putting blames on me, saying that it was all in my mind and that there was nothing going on.

If you think
I am making everything up in my mind
please go ahead and delete your texts
which you kept sending him last night

While I slept next to you
knowing everything that you were doing to me
pretending to play along
if that might make you stay
but in the end, as we all know
love is overrated
and I would drown anyway

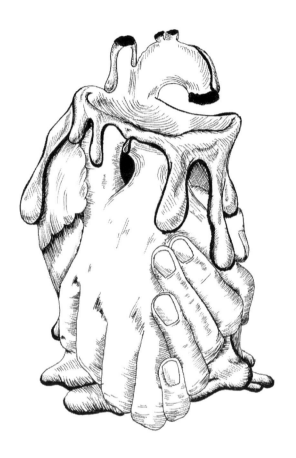

31.

YOU ARE DIFFERENT.

She finally accepted that she liked someone else who could
give her a better future than I ever could.

I could never be him
but that's the whole point
you chose me
because you said I was different

32.

BUT, IS LOVE NOT ENOUGH?

I begged her to not leave me. I don't even remember how much I cried. I knelt down, begging her to not leave me.

I said: "But I love you. Is it not enough?"
She said:" Love is never enough"

33.

BUT LOVE HAPPENS JUST ONCE

Your name still
sparkles my eyes
It gives me butterflies.
You said love happens just once
so, how come you fell in love twice?

34.

HOW COLD ARE YOU?

I listened to her words. They felt sharper than a sword. She knew she was doing wrong, but she did not accept it.

Lies, lies
Hazy skies
so cold hearted, that you
looked deep into my eyes
while telling lies

Covering up
every time
broke my heart
burnt my dreams
took all of me
while giving me nothing

I trusted you
oh, why so, God?
you didn't deserve me
and you knew in your heart

35.

A MILLION LIGHTS IN HER EYES

I saw a million lights
in your eyes
but they were shining for someone else

36.

DO YOU REMEMBER?

In your darkest times
I held you tight
and you whispered
"It feels just alright"

37.

HOW TO ERASE OUR LOVE?

She did not say a word. She barged out of my room like a hurricane. She came back after a few minutes only to hurt me even more. She wanted to break up. She took our pictures and burnt them in front of me. She snapped my phone and deleted all the texts.

"We are done now"- were her last words.

You gave back my letters.
Because of you
I feel so broke
you asked me to erase our memories
but how do I erase our love
will you answer me so?

38.

IF YOU LEAVE,
YOU CAN NEVER COME BACK

If you leave, you can never come back,
'Such a fool', I thought
as if she ever wanted to

39.

AND SHE LEFT WITHOUT
ANY REGRET

I should have realized this before,
Why, every word of yours was flawed.
Why, none of your poems would ever rhyme
maybe
you never intended
to stay beyond this lifetime

40.

A WASTED LOVE STORY:

Like every other love story
our love story ended, too.
But why exactly did I lose you
when I was never meant to?

She was a prayer that was never answered
A pain that left me heart wrenched and shattered

41.

IN AGONY AND IN PAIN

You touched my soul
you shattered my heart
your lies destroyed me
they are still tearing me apart
they said love will bring butterflies,
what those people say is not true.
If I have to die to bring you back
I would happily do that, too

Do you still miss me like I miss you?
Because I am literally dying
every second because of you

42.

WHAT LOVE DID TO ME.

I literally went into depression. I was not in my senses anymore. Never in my life had I imagined that she would be the reason we would not survive.

Crushed jeans,
drowsy me,
rolling up a cigarette
making clouds out of it
sick of people staring
thinking I am mean

Exactly how you hated
me rolling a joint
Do I have to care now
because you are not here anymore?

Do I have to pretend to be sober?
Do I have to fake that I'm fine?
when my clothes smell of dust
and my breath smells of wine

Memories are still there
still the same am I
but you decided to walk away
and fit in someone's else life

43.

PAINFUL REALIZATION

It is so painful
when you realize
that your dream love story
will always remain in your dreams

44.

THE PAIN. OH, THIS PAIN

You know what hurts the most?
Not that you left
but that you moved on so fast
that I wonder if I ever
meant anything to you

45.

HAVE I MOVED ON?

Sometimes there would be days when I would go on without thinking about her, and sometimes, she would be all over my mind. I guess moving on takes a lot of time.

I saw a dream
and you were not in it
I guess I have moved on
but wait, why am I even
thinking about it?

They say time will make it better?
Will it ever?

46.

SOMEWHERE IN THE
PARALLEL WORLD:

I know you are not in my present anymore, but I am too afraid to let go of your memories, so I assume we both are still together in parallel worlds.

I try to imagine
how we used to be happy
how we would stay together
and now that you are with
someone new,
does he even know
your secrets
like I do?
no matter what he says
you and I would always
belong together
maybe in a parallel world
where you would stick with your words
and would choose to stay

Do you ever call him by my name, sometimes?
Because I was your first ever love
and your first ever crime

47.

AND THEN I SAW YOUR PICTURES ONLINE

Even though I had blocked you off my social media accounts, I had a sudden urge to check upon you which was so strong that I unblocked only to see that you were so happy without me.

I saw your pictures
that you posted online

It just hit me like a bullet
upon seeing how you smiled
you look so happy
like you pretended to be with me
I hope he hurts you
the way you hurt me

48.

WHAT HURTS THE MOST?

You know what hurts the most?
That the promises you made with me
are the same promises
you are living with someone else

You were everything
that my heart ever wanted
and he was everything you ever dreamt of.
I am happy that you won

49.

REALIZING THAT YOU WERE NOT SPECIAL

It took me a long time to realize that the stories I told her about my insecurities, were the same ones she used, to leave me.

You broke me into a million pieces
Just like other people broke me, too

50.

REMINISCENCE:

Even though it's been a year now, I still stumble across upon our memories. Your scent, fragrance and you.

Someone was wearing
the same perfume
that you used to wear
and my heart started beating
in pain and fear

51.

CAN WE MEET
FOR ONE LAST TIME?

Sometimes, someone who was your world, destroys you in a million pieces, but you still want to meet that person for one last time to get the closure that your mind and heart needs.

I know we are not together anymore
And we won't be together ever again
But I want to meet you for one last time
To live our moments again
That I can preserve for a lifetime
To get the closure my heart desires
And my mind needs
So I can finally, finally be at peace

I am still standing where you left me
At least tell me whether you would come?

52.

SHALL I FIND SOMEONE ELSE?

I am irreparable
beyond words.
I am not looking for someone, now
because I know, in the end
love will definitely hurt

53.

AM I AFRAID
OF NEW BEGINNINGS?

My heart is still stuck on you
my mind says to move on,
move on with someone new,
my only worry is,
what if she turns out to be
just like you?

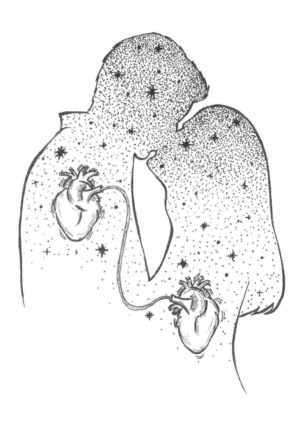

54.

LET'S GO SOMEWHERE NEW

I wanted to run from this place which reminded me of you every second. I wanted to meet new people, but I was not ready to fall in love again.

Let's move to a new place,
where no one knows my name,
and I know they will start judging,
as everyone is just the same.

But till then,
let me find a new love,
new memories to let go of my pain,
you can take my hand,
and please ask me to dance in the rain.

So, maybe this time, I can be with someone else without falling in love. At least I will be able to move on. But I know that I can never be someone I do not desire.

I hope you understand that I cannot stay for long,
because even if I do,
it won't make us strong,
so, please let me go,
try to forget me soon,
I can never be your sunshine,
but maybe I will be your moon.

55.

I WISH YOU WOULD CALL ME.

I still have
unanswered questions
to be resolved,
some memories
to unblock,
a bond to revive,
because you are still
in my mind
like a broken record

56.

THE FINAL CONVERSATION:

She finally called to apologize after countless hours. She wanted to have a conversation with me. She was at her lowest. I could have kept the phone down but I did not. I was not as cold hearted as she once was with me. She drowned me into a sea of depression and let me lie there for 400 days. But still, my heart, my stupid heart melted the moment she said hello.

Sia: "Hi. How are you? Are you fine?

Siddhartha:

"I hate to say
but because of you
I am not doing okay"

Sia: "I know I have done a lot of wrong things. I don't even know if you would want to talk to me. Can you listen to me? I have to justify myself."

Siddhartha:

"I don't want any justification now
you did whatever you wanted to do
and I'm just a stranger for you somehow

You told me that the promises
we made
were infinite
tell me, then,
how did he enter
our love story
and snatch my lifeline?"

She started telling me what he did to her and I was not amused to listen to her painful story, because that's not true love. I never wanted her to be sad, even though she destroyed me.

"I heard he lied
made you cry
I should feel so amused
But I'm not, why?

He texted other girls
while you waited for him
is it not the same
as what you did to me?

Now you know how it feels,
how bad it could hurt,
when you place everything onto someone
and that person betrays your trust

Your mind is fogged,
all memories becoming hazed,
dreams would turn jaded
and you would feel like
you are stuck in a maze"

Sia: "I realize what I did to you. I learnt my lesson. I can't even explain how guilty I am feeling. I want to come back. Please forgive me."

Siddhartha:
"Once I saw you,
I knew
I would never fall in love again
with anyone else
and you knew that too.
Still, you played"

Sia: "I made a lot of terrible mistakes. I thought he was perfect and hence I chose him over you."

Siddhartha:
"I know I am not perfect,
but neither were you
still, I accepted because
that's what lovers do"

Sia: "Why did you let me go?"

Siddhartha:
"You wanted to leave
And I was no longer a good enough reason
To make you stay
So, I let you go"

Sia: "I realized the meaning of love. He did what I did to you and I could understand it was so wrong. He never fought for me like you did."

Siddhartha:

> "I would have gone beyond the world
> to the other side to find you
> but for the first time I was left wondering if
> you were even worth the pain?"

Sia: "I love you, and I am sorry."

Siddhartha: "I can't be with you because I love myself more than I love you. When you drowned me in a whirlwind, I laid there waiting for your hand to pick me up, but you never came. In those dark nights, I picked myself up and fought my demons, all alone."

Sia: "So, what did you realize? Am I worth the pain?"

Siddhartha: "After many sleepless nights, I realized that the answer is no. You are not worth the pain. Someone who could leave me in a blink of an eye could never be worth the pain."

Sia: "Do you love someone else?"

Siddhartha:

> "I knew you were gone
> and there were billons of people around,
> but still no one was enough
> to replace you"

Sia: "Don't you want to get back together?"

Siddhartha:

> You know why I don't want you back?
> Because you made me doubt myself.
> It took me hundreds of days to fix
> What you broke in just one day.
> You took away my light, hope, and shining rays

Sia: "How did you move on?"

Siddhartha: "By realizing that you were not my entire life. Just a tiny part of it."

Sia: "So, was our love fake?"

Siddhartha:
>Just pretend none of this was ever true
>things just happened
>and we outgrew
>this does not mean that
>our love was fake
>I could still give my breath away
>to make you stay
>but I choose not to.

57.

WHY DID SHE EVER COME IN MY LIFE?

The best lesson life taught me was to meet her. Even if our destiny would remain the same, I would still meet her a million times over, only to love myself in the end.

It's finally ok for me
to realize
that it did not work
and it's totally alright.
I discovered myself
while I tried uncovering you.
Thanks for the lesson that
I needed in my life
to become a person I would become
and understand that someday, someone will choose me
over everyone else
because I would be worth it for her
in this lifetime

58.

MOVING ON WAS NOT EASY, BUT WORTH IT

I cried and cried and cried
and just like that,
my tears stopped,
and she was no longer
that someone
whom I wanted to hold

Move on
because
you are way too precious
to be lost due to a stubborn heart
that did not fit
with yours.

The journey from-
"I am glad to meet you" to
"I wonder why I met you"
was unbearably painful
to be told in simple words.
Hence, I will leave it up to you to think of
why our love story did not work

59.

WILL I EVER MEET SOMEONE NEW?

In the luscious
green fields
where the cloudy skies
meet the aqua seas,
I will find my soulmate there

Made in the USA
Monee, IL
02 March 2022

92162231R00067